My leathergirl

Journal

1st Edition

Adynaton Publishing

My leathergirl Journal
Copyright © 2021 by Vincent Andrews

Book Concept and design by:
Vincent Andrews and C. Ryer

Based on the book by:
Tyesha Best

First Edition
Published by Adynaton Publishing.

ISBN 978-1-995748-00-1

ADYNATON
PUBLISHING℠

www. Adynaton Publishing .com

How to use this Journal

When most people think of a journal, they assume it is nothing more than a log of their day. It is actually more than that. It provides insight to a Dominant about the well-being and mental status of their submissive. So, not only is this book a tool to record your personal history, journey, and growth. It also serves as a way for you to share your anxiety, apprehension, fears, joys, happy moments, and overall feelings.

So, how is this beneficial?

It brings stability to what could be otherwise considered chaos. Rather than face-to-face confrontations, it allows the leathergirl to write their thoughts down and express, in writing, their individual state emotionally, economically, physically, along with their activities. However, there are rules to journaling.

RULES

1. Dominants should never punish a submissive for what they write. No exceptions!
2. Journals should always be accessible to the Dominant.
3. Nothing written should be shared outside the dynamic.
4. Dominants should initial the pages, signaling they have read the journal to the submissive.
5. Dominants should make time to read the journals often as possible.

I don't know what your destiny will be, but one thing I do know: the only ones among you who will be really happy are those who have sought and found how to serve.

~Albert Schweitzer

My leathergirl Journal

This Journal belongs to:

Remember, *The leatherboy Handbook*'s originated from the personal journaling of the author Vince Andrews. Using this tool, he created the handbooks that helped provide knowledge and information based on his experiences to hundreds of leatherboys and their Dominants.

How often you write is up to you, but you should do it often. Use this tool to succeed and record your journey.

Volume #_____

Date:_____

-Through-

Date:_____

Dominant Initials_____

Dominant Initials_____

Dominant Initials_____

Dominant Initials_____

Dominant Initials_____

Dominant Initials_____

Dominant Initials_____

Dominant Initials_____

Dominant Initials_____

Dominant Initials_____

Dominant Initials_____

Dominant Initials_____

Dominant Initials_____

Dominant Initials_____

Dominant Initials_____

Dominant Initials_____

Dominant Initials_____

Dominant Initials_____

Dominant Initials_____

I slept and dreamt that life was a joy. I awoke and saw that life was service. I acted and behold; service was joy.

~Rabindranath Tagore

Dominant Initials_____

My leathergirl Journal

Dominant Initials_____

Dominant Initials_____

My leathergirl Journal

Dominant Initials_____

Dominant Initials_____

Dominant Initials_____

Dominant Initials_____

Dominant Initials_____

Dominant Initials_____

Dominant Initials_____

My leathergirl Journal

Dominant Initials_____

Dominant Initials_____

Dominant Initials_____

Dominant Initials_____

Dominant Initials_____

Dominant Initials_____

Dominant Initials_____

Dominant Initials_____

Dominant Initials_____

Dominant Initials_____

Dominant Initials_____

> *The mystical bond of brotherhood makes all men brothers.*
>
> ~Thomas Carlyle

Dominant Initials_____

Dominant Initials_____

Dominant Initials_____

Dominant Initials_____

My leathergirl Journal

Dominant Initials_____

Dominant Initials_____

Dominant Initials_____

Dominant Initials_____

My leathergirl Journal

Dominant Initials_____

Dominant Initials_____

Dominant Initials_____

Dominant Initials_____

Dominant Initials_____

Dominant Initials_____

Dominant Initials_____

Dominant Initials_____

Dominant Initials_____

Dominant Initials_____

Dominant Initials_____

Dominant Initials_____

Dominant Initials_____

> *There are only two creatures of value on the face of the earth: those with commitment; and those who require the commitment of others.*
>
> ~John Adams

Dominant Initials_____

Dominant Initials_____

Dominant Initials_____

Dominant Initials_____

Dominant Initials_____

Dominant Initials_____

Dominant Initials_____

Dominant Initials_____

Dominant Initials_____

Dominant Initials_____

Dominant Initials_____

Dominant Initials_____

Dominant Initials_____

Dominant Initials_____

Dominant Initials_____

Dominant Initials_____

Dominant Initials_____

Dominant Initials_____

Dominant Initials_____

The life of a man consists not in seeing visions and in dreaming dreams, but in active charity and in willing service.

~Henry Longfellow

Dominant Initials_____

Dominant Initials_____

Dominant Initials_____

Dominant Initials_____

Dominant Initials_____

Dominant Initials_____

My leathergirl Journal

Dominant Initials_____

Dominant Initials_____

Dominant Initials_____

Dominant Initials_____

Dominant Initials_____

The best way to find yourself is to lose yourself in the service of others.

~Mahatma Gandhi

Dominant Initials_____

Dominant Initials_____

Dominant Initials_____

Dominant Initials_____

Dominant Initials_____

Dominant Initials_____

Dominant Initials_____

Dominant Initials_____

Dominant Initials_____

Dominant Initials_____

Dominant Initials_____

Dominant Initials_____

Dominant Initials_____

Dominant Initials_____

Dominant Initials_____

Dominant Initials_____

Dominant Initials_____

Dominant Initials_____

Dominant Initials_____

Dominant Initials_____

Dominant Initials_____

Dominant Initials_____

Dominant Initials_____

Dominant Initials_____

Dominant Initials_____

Dominant Initials_____

Dominant Initials_____

Dominant Initials_____

Dominant Initials_____

Dominant Initials_____

Dominant Initials_____

Dominant Initials_____

Dominant Initials_____

Dominant Initials_____

Dominant Initials_____

Dominant Initials_____

Dominant Initials_____

Dominant Initials_____

Dominant Initials_____

Dominant Initials_____

Dominant Initials_____

Dominant Initials_____

Dominant Initials_____

Dominant Initials_____

Dominant Initials_____

Dominant Initials_____

Dominant Initials_____

Dominant Initials_____

Dominant Initials_____

_____

> *Do not be like servants who serve their masters expecting to receive a reward; be rather like servants who serve their master unconditionally, with no thought of reward.*
>
> ~Antigonus of Sokho

Dominant Initials_____

Dominant Initials_____

Dominant Initials_____

Dominant Initials_____

Dominant Initials_____

Dominant Initials_____

Dominant Initials_____

Dominant Initials_____

Dominant Initials_____

Dominant Initials_____

Dominant Initials_____

Dominant Initials_____

Dominant Initials_____

Dominant Initials_____

Dominant Initials_____

Dominant Initials_____

Dominant Initials_____

Dominant Initials_____

My leathergirl Journal

Dominant Initials_____

Dominant Initials_____

My leathergirl Journal

Dominant Initials_____

Dominant Initials_____

My leathergirl Journal

Dominant Initials_____

Dominant Initials_____

My leathergirl Journal

Dominant Initials_____

Dominant Initials_____

Dominant Initials_____

Dominant Initials_____

Dominant Initials_____

Human service is the highest form of self-interest for the person who serves.

~Elbert Hubbard

Dominant Initials_____

> *Human service is the highest form of self-interest for the person who serves.*
>
> ~Elbert Hubbard

Dominant Initials_____

Dominant Initials_____

Dominant Initials_____

Dominant Initials_____

Dominant Initials_____

Dominant Initials_____

Dominant Initials_____

Dominant Initials_____

Dominant Initials_____

Dominant Initials_____

Dominant Initials_____

Dominant Initials_____

The life of a man consists not in seeing visions and in dreaming dreams, but in active charity and in willing service.

~Henry Longfellow

Dominant Initials_____

Dominant Initials_____

Dominant Initials_____

Dominant Initials_____

Dominant Initials_____

Dominant Initials_____

It's time for you to check-in with your Dominant. It is often recommended that submissive and their Dominant sit down and review their goals together. Some things to review are:

- Educational goals
- New responsibilities
- Protocols, both public and private
- Rewards
- Punishments
- Permissions
- Private time together
- Play
- Any family issues
- Work conflicts
- Financial concerns
- Exercise
- Travel plans
- Play partners
- **Order your next journal**

    Anything you can think of that will help you both succeed in a happy, healthy dynamic!

Made in the USA
Middletown, DE
24 September 2023

39256057R00118